Magnificat and Nunc Di

in D minor

Magnificat

Thomas Attwood Walmisley

Thomas Attwood Walmisley

Magnificat and Nunc Dimittis
in D minor

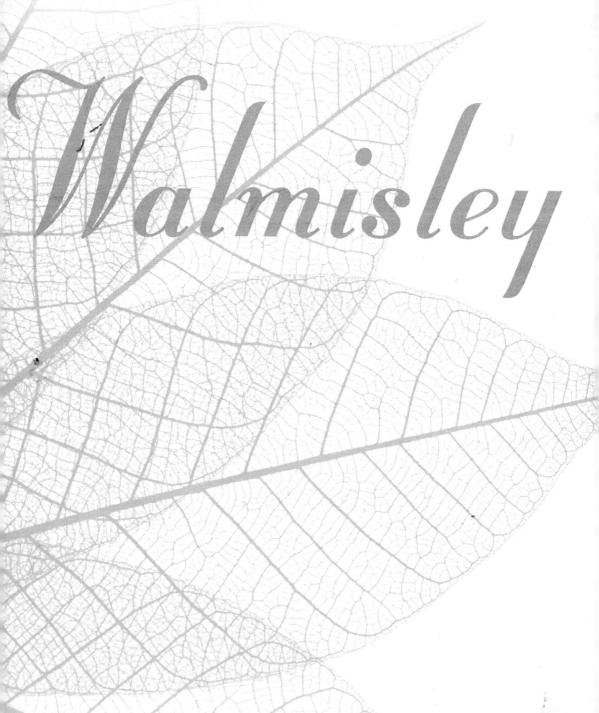

Novello Publishing Limited

SATB

THOMAS ATTWOOD WALMISLEY
MAGNIFICAT AND NUNC DIMITTIS IN D MINOR

Thomas Walmisley, a troubled Renaissance man who excelled in music, literature and mathematics alike, shares some credit with S. S. Wesley for setting Anglican music on a new path.

He studied under Thomas Attwood, his godfather, after whom he was named. Attwood, who had been a favourite pupil of Mozart, played a large part in introducing the Viennese master's work to English audiences. Walmisley proved worthy in the face of his distinguished heritage: as professor of music at Cambridge University, he instigated public lectures in music at which he predicted the rise of the music of a man called Bach to nonplussed audiences.

His Canticles in D minor marked the beginnings of a more complex interaction between choir and organ in the liturgy. They were, significantly, to prove influential for Charles Villiers Stanford, one of his successors at Trinity College, Cambridge.

Published by
Novello Publishing Limited
14-15 Berners Street,
London W1T 3LJ, UK.

Exclusive Distributors:
Music Sales Limited
Distribution Centre, Newmarket Road,
Bury St Edmunds, Suffolk IP33 3YB, UK.

Music Sales Pty Limited
20 Resolution Drive, Caringbah,
NSW 2229, Australia.

Order No. NOV291995
ISBN 978-1-84938-905-1

Edited by Jonathan Wikeley.
Notes by Thomas Lydon.

Printed in the EU.

www.chesternovello.com

NOVELLO PUBLISHING LIMITED

6

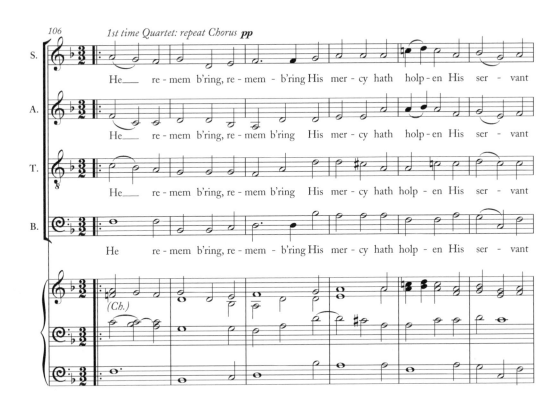

* Bass from an Agnus Dei by Henri Dumont

Nunc Dimittis

16

* Bass from an Amen by Henri Dumont

56789

NOVELLO SACRED CHORAL MUSIC

A selection of some of the finest church music ever written, newly engraved and published by Novello Publishing in clear, attractive editions.

ADOLPHE ADAM
O Holy Night
NOV291819

EDGAR BAINTON
And I Saw A New Heaven
NOV291896

EDWARD BAIRSTOW
Save Us, O Lord
NOV291984

JOHANNES BRAHMS
How Lovely Are Thy Dwellings
NOV291808

HERBERT BREWER
Magnificat and Nunc Dimittis in D
NOV291907

HENRY BALFOUR GARDINER
Evening Hymn
NOV291874

PATRICK HADLEY
My Beloved Spake
NOV291962

EDWARD NAYLOR
Vox dicentis, clama
NOV291951

JOSEPH HAYDN
The Heavens Are Telling
NOV291863

Insanae et vanae curae
NOV291885

JOHN STAINER
I Saw The Lord
NOV291852

CHARLES VILLIERS STANFORD
Jubilate in B flat
NOV291841

Magnificat and Nunc Dimittis in B flat
NOV291918

Magnificat and Nunc Dimittis in A
NOV291940

THOMAS ATTWOOD WALMISLEY
Magnificat and Nunc Dimittis in D minor
NOV291995

SAMUEL SEBASTIAN WESLEY
Blessed Be The God And Father
NOV291929

Ascribe Unto The Lord
NOV291973

CHARLES WOOD
Magnificat and Nunc Dimittis in D
NOV291830

NOV291995
Cover photo courtesy of istock
ISBN 978-1-84938-905-1

NOV291995
TJ
09/13
E
£1.99

Novello Publishing Limited
14/1... ...ter, London W1T 3LJ, UK.
Ex... ...s Distributors Music Sales Limited
Newmarket Road, B...ry St Edmunds, Suf... UK.
...chester...com

9 781849 389051